My best Mum

Written by Anna Nilsen
Illustrated by Emma Dodd

My Mum's best at mowing lawns...

My Mum's best at buying clothes...

My Mum's best at finding bargains –

My Mum's best at
washing clothes,

My Mum's best at washing cars...

My Mum's best at wrapping presents.

My Mum's best at taking photos when we're on our holidays.